Maths
made easy

Key Stage 2
ages 9-10
Advanced

Author
John Kennedy

Consultant
Sean McArdle

LONDON • NEW YORK • MUNICH • MELBOURNE • DELHI

Multiplying and dividing

Write the answer in the box.

$26 \times 10 = \boxed{260}$ $26 \times 100 = \boxed{2\,600}$

$431 \div 10 = \boxed{43.1}$ $431 \div 100 = \boxed{4.31}$

Write the answer in the box.

$33 \times 10 =$ ___ $21 \times 10 =$ ___ $42 \times 10 =$ ___

$94 \times 100 =$ ___ $36 \times 100 =$ ___ $81 \times 100 =$ ___

$416 \times 10 =$ ___ $204 \times 10 =$ ___ $513 \times 10 =$ ___

$767 \times 100 =$ ___ $821 \times 100 =$ ___ $245 \times 100 =$ ___

Write the answer in the box.

$127 \div 10 =$ ___ $263 \div 10 =$ ___ $471 \div 10 =$ ___

$112 \div 100 =$ ___ $844 \div 100 =$ ___ $393 \div 100 =$ ___

$25 \div 10 =$ ___ $32 \div 10 =$ ___ $27 \div 10 =$ ___

$51 \div 100 =$ ___ $22 \div 100 =$ ___ $94 \div 100 =$ ___

Find the number that has been multiplied by 100.

___ $\times 100 = 5\,900$ ___ $\times 100 = 71\,400$

___ $\times 100 = 72\,100$ ___ $\times 100 = 23\,400$

___ $\times 100 = 1\,100$ ___ $\times 100 = 47\,000$

___ $\times 100 = 8\,400$ ___ $\times 100 = 44\,100$

Find the number that has been divided by 100.

___ $\div 100 = 3.64$ ___ $\div 100 = 8.5$

___ $\div 100 = 21.37$ ___ $\div 100 = 18.2$

___ $\div 100 = 86.43$ ___ $\div 100 = 21$

___ $\div 100 = 1.05$ ___ $\div 100 = 5.92$

Ordering sets of amounts

Write these amounts in order, starting with the smallest.

70 cm	300 mm	2 km	6 m	500 mm
300 mm	500 mm	70 cm	6 m	2 km

Write these amounts in order, starting with the smallest.

500p	£4.00	£5.50	350p	640p

2 kg	750 g	1 500 g	1.6 kg	300 g

125 min	2 hours	$3\frac{1}{2}$ hours	200 min	$\frac{3}{4}$ hour

2 500 m	2 km	1 000 cm	20 m	1 000 m

£240	3 500p	£125.00	4 600p	£50.00

400 mm	60 cm	12 cm	0.5 m	1 km

0.75 kg	500 g	1 kg	300 g	900 g

2 hours	75 min	$1\frac{1}{2}$ hours	100 min	150 min

44 mm	4 cm	4 m	4 km	40 cm

1 200 m	1 km	750 m	0.5 km	200 m

Calculating temperature rise and fall

The temperature at midnight was –6°C.
By midday it was 4°C. By how much had
the temperature increased?

10°C

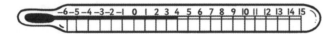

What is the difference in temperature between:

−2°C and 7°C   −5°C and 10°C

−1°C and 7°C   −4°C and 2°C

−7°C and 10°C   −8°C and 5°C

−9°C and −1°C   −11°C and 5°C

−12°C and 0°C   −4°C and 7°C

−3°C and 6°C   −15°C and 21°C

−21°C and 13°C   −19°C and 12°C

Write the answer in the box.

The temperature in Moscow is −5°C. If it rises to 3°C,
by how much has it risen?

The temperature in London is 18°C. If it rises to 25°C,
by how much has it risen?

The temperature in Bangkok is 29°C. The temperature in
Chicago is −3°C. How much warmer than Chicago is Bangkok?

The temperature at 7 a.m. is −3°C. At noon it is 7°C. By how
much has it risen?

The thermometer in a garage reads 8°C. If it has risen 11°C since
6 a.m., what was the temperature then?

The temperature inside a house is 17°C. Outside it is −4°C.
How much warmer is it inside than outside?

Counting in constant steps

Continue each row.

Steps of 3

$-2\frac{1}{2}$	$\frac{1}{2}$	$3\frac{1}{2}$	$6\frac{1}{2}$	$9\frac{1}{2}$	$12\frac{1}{2}$

Steps of 5

3.5	-1.5	-6.5	-11.5	-16.5	-21.5

Continue each row.

$-15\frac{1}{2}$	$-10\frac{1}{2}$	$-5\frac{1}{2}$			
$-5\frac{1}{4}$	$-3\frac{1}{4}$	$-1\frac{1}{4}$			
$-8\frac{1}{3}$	$-7\frac{1}{3}$	$-6\frac{1}{3}$		$-4\frac{1}{3}$	
$5\frac{1}{4}$	$-4\frac{3}{4}$	$-14\frac{3}{4}$			
$12\frac{1}{2}$	$8\frac{1}{2}$	$4\frac{1}{2}$			$-7\frac{1}{2}$

7.5	5.5	3.5			
9.4	5.4	1.4		-6.6	
11.6	3.6	-4.4			
-6.3	-2.3	1.7			
-12.1	-7.1	-2.1			12.9
-14.6	-7.6	-0.6			

$1\frac{1}{2}$	$-3\frac{1}{2}$	$-8\frac{1}{2}$			
-8.4	-5.4	-2.4		3.6	
$-7\frac{1}{4}$	$-1\frac{1}{4}$	$4\frac{3}{4}$			$22\frac{3}{4}$
7.5	-1.5	-10.5			

Products of odd and even numbers

Find the products of these numbers.

3 and 4   The product of 3 and 4 is 12.   6 and 8   The product of 6 and 8 is 48.

Find the products of these odd and even numbers.

5 and 6 _____   3 and 2 _____

7 and 4 _____   8 and 3 _____

6 and 3 _____   2 and 9 _____

10 and 3 _____   12 and 5 _____

What do you notice about your answers? _____

_____

Find the products of these odd numbers.

5 and 7 _____   3 and 9 _____

5 and 11 _____   7 and 3 _____

9 and 5 _____   11 and 7 _____

13 and 3 _____   1 and 5 _____

What do you notice about your answers? _____

_____

Find the products of these even numbers.

2 and 4 _____   4 and 6 _____

6 and 2 _____   4 and 8 _____

10 and 2 _____   4 and 10 _____

6 and 10 _____   6 and 8 _____

What do you notice about your answers? _____

_____

Can you write a rule for the products of odd and even numbers?

_____

Squares of numbers

Find the square of 2.

$$2 \times 2 = 4$$

What is the area of this square?

2 cm

2 cm

$$2 \times 2 = 4$$
$$\text{area} = 4 \text{ cm}^2$$

Find the square of these numbers.

3   1   6

7   8   5

9   4   10

Now try these.

13   20   40

11   12   30

What are the areas of these squares?

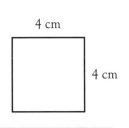

4 cm

4 cm

cm^2

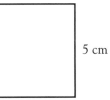

5 cm

5 cm

cm^2

6 cm

6 cm

cm^2

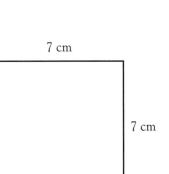

7 cm

7 cm

cm^2

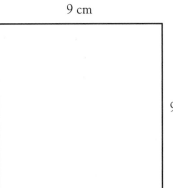

9 cm

9 cm

cm^2

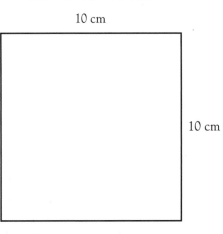

10 cm

10 cm

cm^2

Factors of numbers from 66 to 100

The factors of 66 are   1   2   3   6   11   22   33   66

Circle the factors of 94.   (1)   (2)   (47)   28   32   (94)   86   43   71

Write the factors of each number in the box.

The factors of 70 are

The factors of 85 are

The factors of 69 are

The factors of 83 are

The factors of 75 are

The factors of 96 are

The factors of 63 are

The factors of 99 are

The factors of 72 are

Circle the factors of 68.

    1   2   3   4   5   6   7   8   9   11   12   17   34   35   62   68

Circle the factors of 95.

    1   2   3   4   5   15   16   17   19   24   37   85   90   95   96

Circle the factors of 88.

    1   2   3   4   5   6   8   10   11   15   22   25   27   44   87   88

Circle the factors of 73.

    1   2   4   5   6   8   9   10   12   13   14   15   30   60   73

Some numbers only have factors of 1 and themselves. They are called prime numbers.
Write down all the prime numbers between 66 and 100 in the box.

Changing fractions

Change these top-heavy fractions to mixed numbers.

$$\frac{17}{10} = \quad 1\frac{7}{10} \qquad\qquad \frac{25}{6} = \quad 4\frac{1}{6}$$

Change this top-heavy fraction to a mixed number. Remember you may need to cancel.

$$\frac{16}{10} = \quad 1\frac{\cancel{6}^{3}}{\cancel{10}_{5}} = 1\frac{3}{5}$$

Change these top-heavy fractions to mixed numbers. Remember you may need to cancel.

$\frac{15}{4} =$ $\frac{13}{10} =$ $\frac{29}{5} =$

$\frac{19}{12} =$ $\frac{22}{9} =$ $\frac{17}{6} =$

$\frac{19}{6} =$ $\frac{24}{5} =$ $\frac{13}{3} =$

$\frac{13}{4} =$ $\frac{21}{2} =$ $\frac{14}{9} =$

$\frac{9}{8} =$ $\frac{11}{6} =$ $\frac{15}{7} =$

$\frac{17}{8} =$ $\frac{43}{4} =$ $\frac{11}{5} =$

$\frac{16}{10} =$ $\frac{36}{8} =$ $\frac{18}{8} =$

$\frac{45}{10} =$ $\frac{22}{6} =$ $\frac{24}{20} =$

$\frac{26}{8} =$ $\frac{20}{8} =$ $\frac{16}{12} =$

$\frac{25}{15} =$ $\frac{18}{4} =$ $\frac{20}{14} =$

$\frac{28}{24} =$ $\frac{32}{6} =$ $\frac{26}{10} =$

$\frac{18}{12} =$ $\frac{46}{4} =$ $\frac{30}{9} =$

Ordering sets of decimals

Write these decimals in order starting with the smallest.

0.45	0.21	2.07	1.45	3.62	2.17
0.21	0.45	1.45	2.07	2.17	3.62

Write these decimals in order starting with the smallest.

5.63	2.14	5.6	3.91	1.25	4.63

9.39	0.24	7.63	8.25	7.49	9.40

1.05	2.36	1.09	2.41	7.94	1.50

3.92	5.63	2.29	4.62	5.36	2.15

28.71	21.87	27.18	21.78	28.17	27.81

Write these amounts in order starting with the smallest.

£56.25	£32.40	£11.36	£32.04	£55.26	£36.19

94.21 km	87.05 km	76.91 km	94.36 km	65.99 km	110.75 km

26.41 kg	47.23 kg	26.14 kg	35.23 kg	49.14 kg	35.32 kg

19.51 m	16.15 m	15.53 m	12.65 m	24.24 m	16.51 m

7.35 l	8.29 l	5.73 l	8.92 l	10.65 l	4.29 l

Percentages as fractions of 100

Write these fractions as percentages.

$$\frac{7}{10} = \boxed{70\%} \qquad\qquad \frac{1}{5} = \boxed{20\%}$$

Write this percentage as a fraction.

$$65\% = \frac{\overset{13}{\cancel{65}}}{\underset{20}{\cancel{100}}} = \frac{13}{20}$$

Write these fractions as percentages.

$$\frac{2}{5} = \boxed{} \qquad \frac{3}{10} = \boxed{} \qquad \frac{1}{2} = \boxed{}$$

$$\frac{9}{10} = \boxed{} \qquad \frac{3}{5} = \boxed{} \qquad \frac{4}{5} = \boxed{}$$

$$\frac{1}{10} = \boxed{} \qquad \frac{1}{4} = \boxed{} \qquad \frac{3}{4} = \boxed{}$$

Now try these.

$$\frac{3}{100} = \boxed{} \qquad \frac{7}{100} = \boxed{} \qquad \frac{9}{100} = \boxed{}$$

$$\frac{23}{100} = \boxed{} \qquad \frac{47}{100} = \boxed{} \qquad \frac{93}{100} = \boxed{}$$

Change these percentages to fractions. Remember that you may need to cancel.

$$20\% = \boxed{} \qquad 45\% = \boxed{} \qquad 55\% = \boxed{}$$

$$12\% = \boxed{} \qquad 35\% = \boxed{} \qquad 60\% = \boxed{}$$

Work out the answer to each sum.
Cyril ate $\frac{2}{5}$ of a box of chocolates.
What percentage did he have left?

Tasmin put a 10% deposit on a dress in the
sale. What fraction of the price did she
still have to pay?

Working out percentages

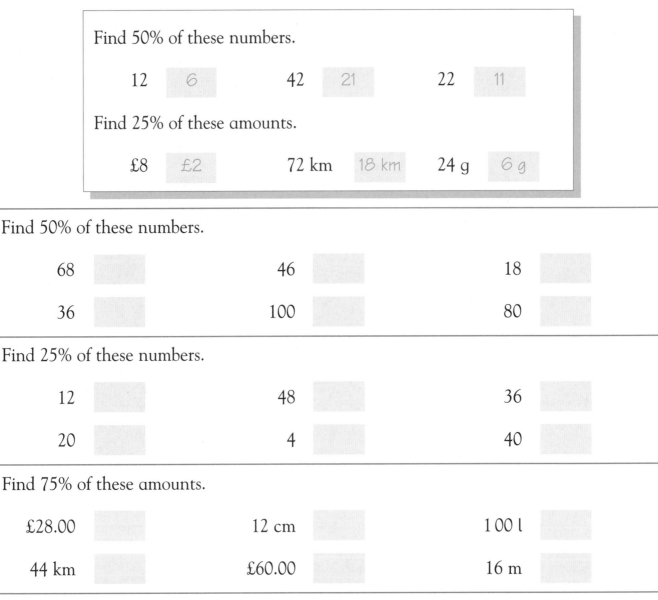

Find 50% of these numbers.

12　　6　　　　42　　21　　　　22　　11

Find 25% of these amounts.

£8　　£2　　　　72 km　　18 km　　24 g　　6 g

Find 50% of these numbers.

68		46		18	
36		100		80	

Find 25% of these numbers.

12		48		36	
20		4		40	

Find 75% of these amounts.

£28.00		12 cm		1 00 l	
44 km		£60.00		16 m	

Find 10% of these amounts.

£200.00		70 m		30 cm	
24 l		£37.00		48 g	
62 km		27 cm		36 l	

Write the answer in the box.

25% of a number is 12. What is the number?

10% of a number is 14. What is the number?

Mark spent 25% of his money. If he still has
£60, how much did he spend?

Adding numbers in longer lists

Work out the answers to these sums.

```
  £327          1 374 km
  £644          2 362 km
  £923          1 690 km
+ £455        + 4 216 km
 £2 349        9 642 km
  2 1 1          1 2 1
```

Work out the answers to these sums.

```
  539 m         206 m         481 m         735 m
  965 m         812 m         604 m         234 m
  774 m         619 m         274 m         391 m
+ 347 m       + 832 m       + 976 m       + 863 m
     m             m             m             m
```

```
  746 kg        817 kg        944 kg        763 kg
  201 kg        591 kg        835 kg        861 kg
  432 kg        685 kg        391 kg        608 kg
+ 309 kg      + 245 kg      + 105 kg      + 671 kg
    kg            kg            kg            kg
```

```
  6 329 m       5 245 m       6 431 m       8 690 m
  3 251 m       2 845 m       7 453 m       5 243 m
  2 642 m       1 937 m       4 650 m       6 137 m
+ 4 823 m     + 5 610 m     + 3 782 m     + 5 843 m
      m             m             m             m
```

```
  £4 721        £3 654        £8 172        £4 352
  £1 711        £5 932        £1 475        £3 920
  £8 342        £6 841        £7 760        £8 439
+ £2 365      + £4 736      + £8 102      + £1 348
  £             £             £             £
```

```
  1 573 km      4 902 km      3 756 km      8 010 km
  6 231 km      7 547 km      1 150 km      7 793 km
  2 112 km      8 463 km      5 535 km      1 641 km
+ 2 141 km    + 6 418 km    + 3 852 km    + 7 684 km
     km            km            km            km
```

Adding numbers in longer lists

Work out the answers to these sums.

3 461 km	£3 645
2 100 km	£4 231
3 522 km	£8 560
4 159 km	£7 213
+ 3 614 km	+ £9 463
16 856 km	£33 112
1 11	2 21

Work out the answers to these sums.

3 144 m	2 510 m	3 276 m	1 475 m
2 345 m	1 734 m	1 593 m	2 653 m
8 479 m	5 421 m	6 837 m	2 765 m
1 004 m	3 205 m	1 769 m	3 742 m
+ 6 310 m	+ 2 365 m	+ 3 846 m	+5 905 m
m	m	m	m

£1 480	£4 527	£3 063	£8 741
£6 366	£8 309	£8 460	£6 334
£1 313	£6 235	£2 712	£3 231
£3 389	£4 487	£3 756	£6 063
+ £4 592	+ £4 065	+ £5 650	+ £4 096
£	£	£	£

8 644 km	3 823 km	8 636 km	8 618 km
3 353 km	9 275 km	8 986 km	3 453 km
6 400 km	3 669 km	5 367 km	4 404 km
5 768 km	2 998 km	6 863 km	4 361 km
+ 1 092 km	+ 7 564 km	+ 3 605 km	+5 641 km
km	km	km	km

£3 742	£8 596	£2 739	£8 463
£2 785	£5 430	£6 517	£5 641
£7 326	£8 379	£6 014	£9 430
£1 652	£2 943	£7 115	£8 204
+ £5 753	+ £1 081	+ £2 704	+ £6 326
£	£	£	£

Adding decimal fractions

Write the answer to each sum.

£36.38	27.46 m
+ £22.05	+ 15.81 m
£58.43	43.27 m
1	11 .

Write the answer to each sum.

£14.61	£29.13	£34.71
+ £35.14	+ £62.75	+ £25.78

£26.75	£15.89	£43.65
+ £85.43	+ £79.15	+ £35.10

17.58 m	45.83 m	29.98 m
+ 65.77 m	+ 38.21 m	+ 72.35 m

43.87 m	76.92 m	64.83 m
+ 51.97 m	+ 31.88 m	+ 27.93 m

Write the answer to each sum in the box.

£23.79 + £44.68 =   £52.97 + £84.29 =

£67.29 + £44.82 =   £77.38 + £49.82 =

Work out the answer to each sum.

Sean buys a computer game for £65.99.
He already has one that cost £52.45.
How much has he spent on computer games?

Mrs Kapur's car holds 42.57 litres of petrol.
Her husband's car holds 63.41 litres of petrol.
How much petrol must they buy to fill both cars?

Adding decimal fractions

Write the answer to each sum.

£73.24	84.61 m
+ £16.99	+ 13.98 m
£90.23	98.59 m
1 1	1

Write the answer to each sum.

£28.77	£13.65	£28.99
+ £45.45	+ £37.66	+ £34.93

£17.79	£20.58	£39.76
+ £74.33	+ £69.55	+ £24.34

18.48 m	23.95 m	17.68 m
+ 34.93 m	+ 27.15 m	+ 16.27 m

84.64 m	23.29 m	73.81 m
+ 16.38 m	+ 36.82 m	+ 26.89 m

Write the answer to each sum in the box.

£64.82 + £39.28 =   £97.47 + £29.34 =

£32.91 + £11.39 =   £52.63 + £18.57 =

Work out the answer to each sum.

A family's shopping comes to £67.48
the first week and £84.63 the following
week. How much was spent
over the two weeks?

A builder needs 47.32 metres of skirting for the
downstairs of a house and 36.79 metres for the
upstairs. How much skirting will he use?

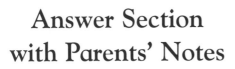

Answer Section with Parents' Notes

Key Stage 2
Ages 9–10
Advanced

This 8-page section provides answers to all the activities in the book. This will enable you to mark your children's work or can be used by them if they prefer to do their own marking.

The notes for each page help explain the common pitfalls and problems and, where appropriate, give indications as to what practice is needed to ensure your children understand where they have gone wrong.

Multiplying and dividing

Write the answer in the box.

26 x 10 = 260	26 x 100 = 2 600
431 ÷ 10 = 43.1	431 ÷ 100 = 4.31

Write the answer in the box.

33 x 10 = 330	21 x 10 = 210	42 x 10 = 420
94 x 100 = 9 400	36 x 100 = 3 600	81 x 100 = 8 100
416 x 10 = 4 160	204 x 10 = 2 040	513 x 10 = 5 130
767 x 100 = 76 700	821 x 100 = 82 100	245 x 100 = 24 500

Write the answer in the box.

127 ÷ 10 = 12.7	263 ÷ 10 = 26.3	471 ÷ 10 = 47.1
112 ÷ 100 = 1.12	844 ÷ 100 = 8.44	393 ÷ 100 = 3.93
25 ÷ 10 = 2.5	32 ÷ 10 = 3.2	27 ÷ 10 = 2.7
51 ÷ 100 = 0.51	22 ÷ 100 = 0.22	94 ÷ 100 = 0.94

Find the number that has been multiplied by 100.

59 x 100 = 5 900	714 x 100 = 71 400
721 x 100 = 72 100	234 x 100 = 23 400
11 x 100 = 1 100	470 x 100 = 47 000
84 x 100 = 8 400	441 x 100 = 44 100

Find the number that has been divided by 100.

364 ÷ 100 = 3.64	850 ÷ 100 = 8.5
2 137 ÷ 100 = 21.37	1 820 ÷ 100 = 18.2
8 643 ÷ 100 = 86.43	2 100 ÷ 100 = 21
105 ÷ 100 = 1.05	592 ÷ 100 = 5.92

Children should realise that multiplying by 10 or 100 means adding one or two noughts to the number, and dividing by 10 or 100 means that the number moves one or two places to the right. In the later sections the inverse operation gives the number that begins the sum.

Ordering sets of amounts

Write these amounts in order, starting with the smallest.

70 cm	300 mm	2 km	6 m	500 mm
300 mm	500 mm	70 cm	6 m	2 km

Write these amounts in order, starting with the smallest.

500p	£4.00	£5.50	350p	640p
350p	£4.00	500p	£5.50	640p
2 kg	750 g	1 500 g	1.6 kg	300 g
300 g	750 g	1500 g	1.6 kg	2 kg
125 min	2 hours	$3\frac{1}{2}$ hours	200 min	$\frac{3}{4}$ hour
$\frac{3}{4}$ hour	2 hours	125 min	200 min	$3\frac{1}{2}$ hours
2 500 m	2 km	1 000 cm	20 m	1 000 m
1000 cm	20 m	1000 m	2 km	2 500 m
£240	3 500p	£125.00	4 600p	£50.00
3500p	4 600p	£50.00	£125.00	£240
400 mm	60 cm	12 cm	0.5 m	1 km
12 cm	400 mm	0.5 m	60 cm	1 km
0.75 kg	500 g	1 kg	300 g	900 g
300 g	500 g	0.75 kg	900 g	1 kg
2 hours	75 min	$1\frac{1}{2}$ hours	100 min	150 min
75 min	$1\frac{1}{2}$ hours	100 min	2 hours	150 min
44 mm	4 cm	4 m	4 km	40 cm
4 cm	44 mm	40 cm	4 m	4 km
1 200 m	1 km	750 m	0.5 m	200 m
200 m	0.5 km	750 m	1 km	1 200 m

The most likely problems on this page will stem from a lack of understanding of the relationship between amounts written in different ways. Look out for confusion between large amounts of small units and small amounts of large units, such as 350p and £4.00.

Calculating temperature rise and fall

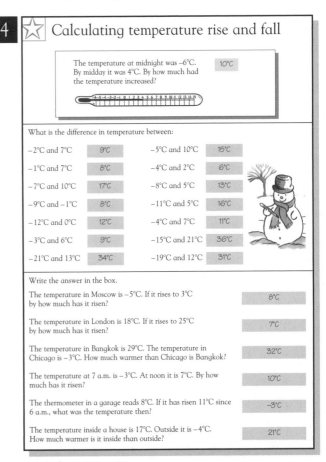

The temperature at midnight was –6°C. By midday it was 4°C. By how much had the temperature increased? **10°C**

What is the difference in temperature between:

–2°C and 7°C	9°C	–5°C and 10°C	15°C
–1°C and 7°C	8°C	–4°C and 2°C	6°C
–7°C and 10°C	17°C	–8°C and 5°C	13°C
–9°C and –1°C	8°C	–11°C and 5°C	16°C
–12°C and 0°C	12°C	–4°C and 7°C	11°C
–3°C and 6°C	9°C	–15°C and 21°C	36°C
–21°C and 13°C	34°C	–19°C and 12°C	31°C

Write the answer in the box.

The temperature in Moscow is –5°C. If it rises to 3°C by how much has it risen? **8°C**

The temperature in London is 18°C. If it rises to 25°C by how much has it risen? **7°C**

The temperature in Bangkok is 29°C. The temperature in Chicago is –3°C. How much warmer than Chicago is Bangkok? **32°C**

The temperature at 7 a.m. is –3°C. At noon it is 7°C. By how much has it risen? **10°C**

The thermometer in a garage reads 8°C. If it has risen 11°C since 6 a.m., what was the temperature then? **–3°C**

The temperature inside a house is 17°C. Outside it is –4°C. How much warmer is it inside than outside? **21°C**

Watch out for children taking away the negative number from the positive; the difference between –2 and 7 may be wrongly calculated as 5. They may need to be shown that the –2 is *added* to the 7 to make 9. Use of a number line may help.

5 Counting in constant steps

Continue each row.

Steps of 3

$-2\frac{1}{2}$	$\frac{1}{2}$	$3\frac{1}{2}$	$6\frac{1}{2}$	$9\frac{1}{2}$	$12\frac{1}{2}$

Steps of 5

3.5	–1.5	–6.5	– 11.5	– 16.5	– 21.5

Continue each row.

$-15\frac{1}{2}$	$-10\frac{1}{2}$	$-5\frac{1}{2}$	$-\frac{1}{2}$	$4\frac{1}{2}$	$9\frac{1}{2}$
$-5\frac{1}{4}$	$-3\frac{1}{4}$	$-1\frac{1}{4}$	$\frac{3}{4}$	$2\frac{3}{4}$	$4\frac{3}{4}$
$-8\frac{1}{3}$	$-7\frac{1}{3}$	$-6\frac{1}{3}$	$-5\frac{1}{3}$	$-4\frac{1}{3}$	$-3\frac{1}{3}$
$5\frac{1}{4}$	$-4\frac{3}{4}$	$-14\frac{3}{4}$	$-24\frac{3}{4}$	$-34\frac{3}{4}$	$-44\frac{3}{4}$
$12\frac{1}{2}$	$8\frac{1}{2}$	$4\frac{1}{2}$	$\frac{1}{2}$	$-3\frac{1}{2}$	$-7\frac{1}{2}$
7.5	5.5	3.5	1.5	–0.5	–2.5
9.4	5.4	1.4	–2.6	– 6.6	–10.6
11.6	3.6	– 4.4	–12.4	–20.4	–28.4
– 6.3	– 2.3	1.7	5.7	9.7	13.7
– 12.1	–7.1	– 2.1	2.9	7.9	12.9
– 14.6	– 7.6	– 0.6	6.4	13.4	20.4
$1\frac{1}{2}$	$-3\frac{1}{2}$	$-8\frac{1}{2}$	$-13\frac{1}{2}$	$-18\frac{1}{2}$	$-23\frac{1}{2}$
– 8.4	– 5.4	– 2.4	0.6	3.6	6.6
$-7\frac{1}{4}$	$-1\frac{1}{4}$	$4\frac{3}{4}$	$10\frac{3}{4}$	$16\frac{3}{4}$	$22\frac{3}{4}$
7.5	– 1.5	– 10.5	–19.5	–28.5	–37.5

Point out that the steps can be found by taking the first number away from the second, the second from the third, and so on. Talk about the 'difference' between numbers, associating this word with subtraction. Be careful with fractions and decimals that cross zero.

6 Products of odd and even numbers

Find the products of these numbers.

3 and 4 The product of 3 and 4 is 12. 6 and 8 The product of 6 and 8 is 48.

Find the products of these odd and even numbers.

5 and 6	30	3 and 2	6
7 and 4	28	8 and 3	24
6 and 3	18	2 and 9	18
10 and 3	30	12 and 5	60

What do you notice about your answers? The product of odd and even numbers is always an even number.

Find the products of these odd numbers.

5 and 7	35	3 and 9	27
5 and 11	55	7 and 3	21
9 and 5	45	11 and 7	77
13 and 3	39	1 and 5	5

What do you notice about your answers? The product of two odd numbers is always an odd number.

Find the products of these even numbers.

2 and 4	8	4 and 6	24
6 and 2	12	4 and 8	32
10 and 2	20	4 and 10	40
6 and 10	60	6 and 8	48

What do you notice about your answers? The product of two even numbers is always an even number.

Can you write a rule for the products of odd and even numbers?
The product of two numbers will always be even unless both numbers are odd.

Where children are asked what they notice, you may need to discuss it with them. When asked to make a rule, accept any formulation as long as it indicates that the concept has been understood.

7 Squares of numbers

Find the square of 2.

2 x 2 = 4

What is the area of this square?

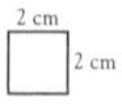

2 cm
2 cm

2 x 2 = 4
area = 4 cm²

Find the square of these numbers.

3	3 x 3 = 9	1	1 x 1 = 1	6	6 x 6 = 36
7	7 x 7 = 49	8	8 x 8 = 64	5	5 x 5 = 25
9	9 x 9 = 81	4	4 x 4 = 16	10	10 x 10 = 100

Now try these.

13	13 x 13 = 169	20	20 x 20 = 400	40	40 x 40 = 1600
11	11 x 11 = 121	12	12 x 12 = 144	30	30 x 30 = 900

What are the areas of these squares?

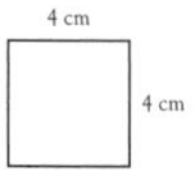

4 cm
4 cm

16 cm²

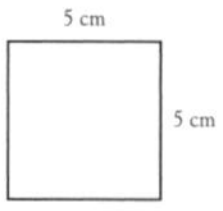

5 cm
5 cm

25 cm²

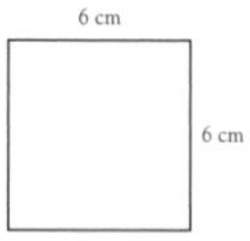

6 cm
6 cm

36 cm²

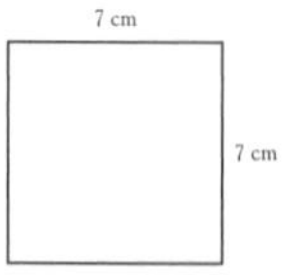

7 cm
7 cm

49 cm²

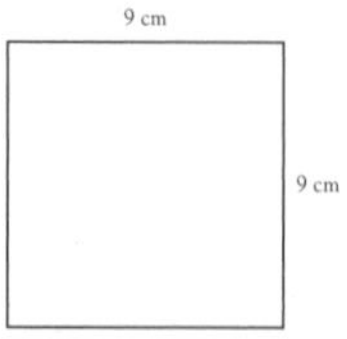

9 cm
9 cm

81 cm²

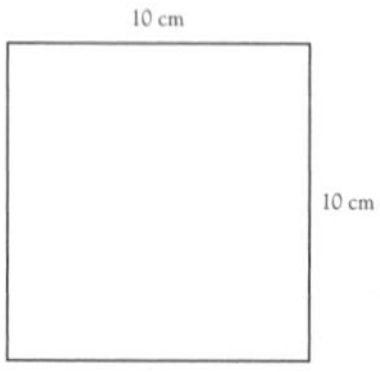

10 cm
10 cm

100 cm²

This page is fairly straightforward. However, check that the children are squaring the number and not multiplying it by two.

8 Factors of numbers from 66 to 100

The factors of 66 are 1 2 3 6 11 22 33 66

Circle the factors of 94. (1) (2) (47) 28 32 (94) 86 43 71

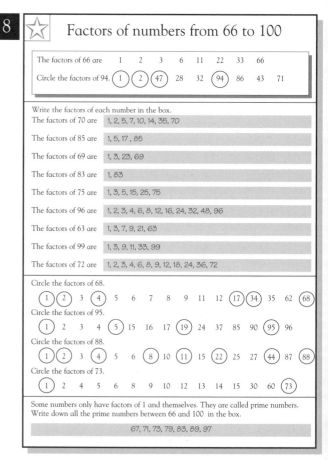

Write the factors of each number in the box.

The factors of 70 are 1, 2, 5, 7, 10, 14, 35, 70

The factors of 85 are 1, 5, 17, 85

The factors of 69 are 1, 3, 23, 69

The factors of 83 are 1, 83

The factors of 75 are 1, 3, 5, 15, 25, 75

The factors of 96 are 1, 2, 3, 4, 6, 8, 12, 16, 24, 32, 48, 96

The factors of 63 are 1, 3, 7, 9, 21, 63

The factors of 99 are 1, 3, 9, 11, 33, 99

The factors of 72 are 1, 2, 3, 4, 6, 8, 9, 12, 18, 24, 36, 72

Circle the factors of 68.
(1) (2) 3 (4) 5 6 7 8 9 11 12 (17) (34) 35 62 (68)

Circle the factors of 95.
(1) 2 3 4 (5) 15 16 17 (19) 24 37 85 90 (95) 96

Circle the factors of 88.
(1) (2) 3 (4) 5 6 (8) 10 (11) 15 (22) 25 27 (44) 87 (88)

Circle the factors of 73.
(1) 2 4 5 6 8 9 10 12 13 14 15 30 60 (73)

Some numbers only have factors of 1 and themselves. They are called prime numbers.
Write down all the prime numbers between 66 and 100 in the box.

67, 71, 73, 79, 83, 89, 97

Quite often some factors of numbers get missed, especially as the numbers get larger. Encourage a systematic method of finding the factors. Children often forget that 1 and itself are factors of a number

Changing fractions

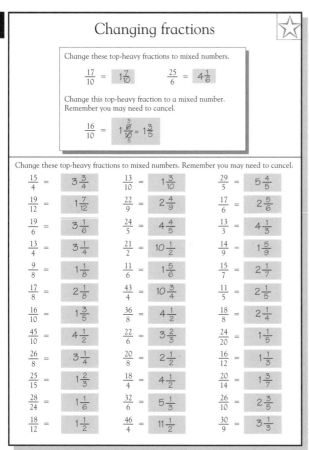

Change these top-heavy fractions to mixed numbers.

$\frac{17}{10} = 1\frac{7}{10}$ $\frac{25}{6} = 4\frac{1}{6}$

Change this top-heavy fraction to a mixed number. Remember you may need to cancel.

$\frac{16}{10} = 1\frac{6}{10} = 1\frac{3}{5}$

Change these top-heavy fractions to mixed numbers. Remember you may need to cancel.

$\frac{15}{4} = 3\frac{3}{4}$	$\frac{13}{10} = 1\frac{3}{10}$	$\frac{29}{5} = 5\frac{4}{5}$
$\frac{19}{12} = 1\frac{7}{12}$	$\frac{22}{9} = 2\frac{4}{9}$	$\frac{17}{6} = 2\frac{5}{6}$
$\frac{19}{6} = 3\frac{1}{6}$	$\frac{24}{5} = 4\frac{4}{5}$	$\frac{13}{3} = 4\frac{1}{3}$
$\frac{13}{4} = 3\frac{1}{4}$	$\frac{21}{2} = 10\frac{1}{2}$	$\frac{14}{9} = 1\frac{5}{9}$
$\frac{9}{8} = 1\frac{1}{8}$	$\frac{11}{6} = 1\frac{5}{6}$	$\frac{15}{7} = 2\frac{1}{7}$
$\frac{17}{8} = 2\frac{1}{8}$	$\frac{43}{4} = 10\frac{3}{4}$	$\frac{11}{5} = 2\frac{1}{5}$
$\frac{16}{10} = 1\frac{3}{5}$	$\frac{36}{8} = 4\frac{1}{2}$	$\frac{18}{8} = 2\frac{1}{4}$
$\frac{45}{10} = 4\frac{1}{2}$	$\frac{22}{6} = 3\frac{2}{3}$	$\frac{24}{20} = 1\frac{1}{5}$
$\frac{26}{8} = 3\frac{1}{4}$	$\frac{20}{8} = 2\frac{1}{2}$	$\frac{16}{12} = 1\frac{1}{3}$
$\frac{25}{15} = 1\frac{2}{3}$	$\frac{18}{4} = 4\frac{1}{2}$	$\frac{20}{14} = 1\frac{3}{7}$
$\frac{28}{24} = 1\frac{1}{6}$	$\frac{32}{6} = 5\frac{1}{3}$	$\frac{26}{10} = 2\frac{3}{5}$
$\frac{18}{12} = 1\frac{1}{2}$	$\frac{46}{4} = 11\frac{1}{2}$	$\frac{30}{9} = 3\frac{1}{3}$

Most children will see that they must divide the denominator into the numerator and place the remainder over denominator. If the child is unclear, use card shapes cut into equal parts to reinforce the idea. Make sure the child simplifies the answers where necessary.

Ordering sets of decimals

Write these decimals in order starting with the smallest.

0.45	0.21	2.07	1.45	3.62	2.17
0.21	0.45	1.45	2.07	2.17	3.62

Write these decimals in order starting with the smallest.

5.63	2.14	5.6	3.91	1.25	4.63
1.25	2.14	3.91	4.63	5.6	5.63
9.39	0.24	7.63	8.25	7.49	9.40
0.24	7.49	7.63	8.25	9.39	9.40
1.05	2.36	1.09	2.41	7.94	1.50
1.05	1.09	1.50	2.36	2.41	7.94
3.92	5.63	2.29	4.62	5.36	2.15
2.15	2.29	3.92	4.62	5.36	5.63
28.71	21.87	27.18	21.78	28.17	27.81
21.78	21.87	27.18	27.81	28.17	28.71

Write these amounts in order starting with the smallest.

£56.25	£32.40	£11.36	£32.04	£55.26	£36.19
£11.36	£32.04	£32.40	£36.19	£55.26	£56.25
94.21 km	87.05 km	76.91 km	94.36 km	65.99 km	110.75 km
65.99 km	76.91 km	87.05 km	94.21 km	94.36 km	110.75 km
26.41 kg	47.23 kg	26.14 kg	35.23 kg	49.14 kg	35.32 kg
26.14 kg	26.41 kg	35.23 kg	35.32 kg	47.23 kg	49.14 kg
19.51 m	16.15 m	15.53 m	12.65 m	24.24 m	16.51 m
12.65 m	15.53 m	16.15 m	16.51 m	19.51 m	24.24 m
7.35 l	8.29 l	5.73 l	8.92 l	10.65 l	4.29 l
4.29 l	5.73 l	7.35 l	8.29 l	8.92 l	10.65 l

Children should look at the units first. If there is more than one number with the same unit, look right to the tenths column for information necessary for sorting. Some numbers use similar digits but with different place values, therefore care is needed.

Percentages as fractions of 100

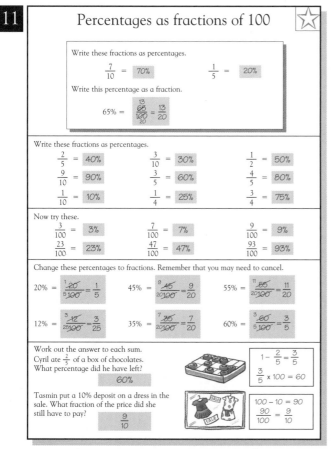

Write these fractions as percentages.

$\frac{7}{10} = 70\%$ $\frac{1}{5} = 20\%$

Write this percentage as a fraction.

$65\% = \frac{65}{100} = \frac{13}{20}$

Write these fractions as percentages.

$\frac{2}{5} = 40\%$	$\frac{3}{10} = 30\%$	$\frac{1}{2} = 50\%$
$\frac{9}{10} = 90\%$	$\frac{3}{5} = 60\%$	$\frac{4}{5} = 80\%$
$\frac{1}{10} = 10\%$	$\frac{1}{4} = 25\%$	$\frac{3}{4} = 75\%$

Now try these.

$\frac{3}{100} = 3\%$	$\frac{7}{100} = 7\%$	$\frac{9}{100} = 9\%$
$\frac{23}{100} = 23\%$	$\frac{47}{100} = 47\%$	$\frac{93}{100} = 93\%$

Change these percentages to fractions. Remember that you may need to cancel.

$20\% = \frac{20}{100} = \frac{1}{5}$ $45\% = \frac{45}{100} = \frac{9}{20}$ $55\% = \frac{55}{100} = \frac{11}{20}$

$12\% = \frac{12}{100} = \frac{3}{25}$ $35\% = \frac{35}{100} = \frac{7}{20}$ $60\% = \frac{60}{100} = \frac{3}{5}$

Work out the answer to each sum.

Cyril ate $\frac{2}{5}$ of a box of chocolates. What percentage did he have left?

60%

$1 - \frac{2}{5} = \frac{3}{5}$

$\frac{3}{5} \times 100 = 60$

Tasmin put a 10% deposit on a dress in the sale. What fraction of the price did she still have to pay?

$\frac{9}{10}$

$100 - 10 = 90$

$\frac{90}{100} = \frac{9}{10}$

Children may need help to see that if $\frac{1}{10}$ is the same as 10%, then $\frac{1}{5}$ is equal to 20% because it is $\frac{2}{10}$. You may have to remind them that 1% is equal to $\frac{1}{100}$. Any number placed over 100 will be the same as the percentage of that number.

Working out percentages

Find 50% of these numbers.

12	6	42	21	22	11

Find 25% of these amounts.

£8	£2	72 km	18 km	24 g	6 g

Find 50% of these numbers.

68	34	46	23	18	9
36	18	100	50	80	40

Find 25% of these numbers.

12	3	48	12	36	9
20	5	4	1	40	10

Find 75% of these amounts.

£28.00	£21.00	12 cm	9 cm	100 l	75 l
44 km	33 km	£60.00	£45.00	16 m	12 m

Find 10% of these amounts.

£200.00	£20.00	70 m	7 m	30 cm	3 cm
24 l	2.4 l	£37.00	£3.70	48 g	4.8 g
62 km	6.2 km	27 cm	2.7 cm	36 l	3.6 l

Write the answer in the box.

25% of a number is 12. What is the number?   48

10% of a number is 14. What is the number?   140

Mark spent 25% of his money. If he still has £60, how much did he spend?   £20

Children should be aware that 50% is equal to $\frac{1}{2}$; 25% is equal to $\frac{1}{4}$; 75% is equal to $\frac{3}{4}$; and 10% is equal to $\frac{1}{10}$. They may convert units e.g. 27 mm is 10% of 27 cm. This shows that they are comfortable with both conversion and percentage sums.

13 — Adding numbers in longer lists

Work out the answers to these sums.

£327	1 374 km
£644	2 362 km
£923	1 690 km
+ £455	+ 4 216 km
£2 349	**9 642 km**

Work out the answers to these sums.

539 m	206 m	481 m	735 m
965 m	812 m	604 m	234 m
774 m	619 m	274 m	391 m
+ 347 m	+ 832 m	+ 976 m	+ 863 m
2 625 m	**2 469 m**	**2 335 m**	**2 223 m**
746 kg	817 kg	944 kg	763 kg
201 kg	591 kg	835 kg	861 kg
432 kg	685 kg	391 kg	608 kg
+ 309 kg	+ 245 kg	+ 105 kg	+ 671 kg
1 688 kg	**2 338 kg**	**2 275 kg**	**2 903 kg**
6 329 m	5 245 m	6 431 m	8 690 m
3 251 m	2 845 m	7 453 m	5 243 m
2 642 m	1 937 m	4 650 m	6 137 m
+ 4 823 m	+ 5 610 m	+ 3 782 m	+ 5 843 m
17 045 m	**15 637 m**	**22 316 m**	**25 913 m**
£4 721	£3 654	£8 172	£4 352
£1 711	£5 932	£1 475	£3 920
£8 342	£6 841	£7 760	£8 439
+ £2 365	+ £4 736	+ £8 102	+ £1 348
£17 139	**£21 163**	**£25 509**	**£18 059**
1 573 km	4 902 km	3 756 km	8 010 km
6 231 km	7 547 km	1 150 km	7 793 km
2 112 km	8 463 km	5 535 km	1 641 km
+ 2 141 km	+ 6 418 km	+ 3 852 km	+ 7 684 km
12 057 km	**27 330 km**	**14 293 km**	**25 128 km**

This page and the next should be fairly straightforward but with larger lists involved there is always the possibility of errors creeping in. Look out for failure to carry or forgetting to add on the numbers that have been carried.

14 — Adding numbers in longer lists

Work out the answers to these sums.

3 461 km	£3 645
2 100 km	£4 231
3 522 km	£8 560
4 159 km	£7 213
+ 3 614 km	+ £9 463
16 856 km	**£33 112**

Work out the answers to these sums.

3 144 m	2 510 m	3 276 m	1 475 m
2 345 m	1 734 m	1 593 m	2 653 m
8 479 m	5 421 m	6 837 m	2 765 m
1 004 m	3 205 m	1 769 m	3 742 m
+ 6 310 m	+ 2 365 m	+ 3 846 m	+5 905 m
21 282 m	**15 235 m**	**17 321 m**	**16 540 m**
£1 480	£4 527	£3 063	£8 741
£6 366	£8 309	£8 460	£6 334
£1 313	£6 235	£2 712	£3 231
£3 389	£4 487	£3 756	£6 063
+ £4 592	+ £4 065	+ £5 650	+ £4 096
£17 140	**£27 623**	**£23 641**	**£28 465**
8 644 km	3 823 km	8 636 km	8 618 km
3 353 km	9 275 km	8 986 km	3 453 km
6 400 km	3 669 km	5 367 km	4 404 km
5 768 km	2 998 km	6 863 km	4 361 km
+ 1 092 km	+ 7 564 km	+ 3 605 km	+5 641 km
25 257 km	**27 329 km**	**33 457 km**	**26 477 km**
£3 742	£8 596	£2 739	£8 463
£2 785	£5 430	£6 517	£5 641
£7 326	£8 379	£6 014	£9 430
£1 652	£2 943	£7 115	£8 204
+ £5 753	+ £1 081	+ £2 704	+ £6 326
£21 258	**£26 429**	**£25 089**	**£38 064**

As with the previous page, problems may arise because of the long list of numbers.

15 — Adding decimal fractions

Write the answer to each sum.

£36.38	27.46 m
+ £22.05	+ 15.81 m
£58.43	**43.27 m**

Write the answer to each sum.

£14.61	£29.13	£34.71
+ £35.14	+£62.75	+ £25.78
£49.75	**£91.88**	**£60.49**
£26.75	£15.89	£43.65
+ £85.43	+£79.15	+ £35.10
£112.18	**£95.04**	**£78.75**
17.58 m	45.83 m	29.98 m
+ 65.77 m	+ 38.21 m	+ 72.35 m
83.35 m	**84.04 m**	**102.33 m**
43.87 m	76.92 m	64.83 m
+ 51.97 m	+ 31.88 m	+ 27.93 m
95.84 m	**108.80 m**	**92.76 m**

Write the answer to each sum in the box.

£23.79 + £44.68 = **£68.47**   £52.97 + £84.29 = **£137.26**

£67.29 + £44.82 = **£112.11**   £77.38 + £49.82 = **£127.20**

Work out the answer to each sum.

Sean buys a computer game for £65.99. He already has one that cost £52.45. How much has he spent on computer games?

65.99
+ 52.45
118.44

£118.44

Mrs Kapur's car holds 42.57 litres of petrol. Her husband's car holds 63.41 litres of petrol. How much petrol must they buy to fill both cars?

42.57
+ 63.41
105.98

105.98 l

This page and the next should follow on from the earlier addition work. The most likely error will be misplacing the decimal point when adding horizontally. Less confident children may need to be reassured when carrying across the decimal point.

16 — Adding decimal fractions

Write the answer to each sum.

£73.24	84.61 m
+ £16.99	+ 13.98 m
£90.23	**98.59 m**

Write the answer to each sum.

£28.77	£13.65	£28.99
+£45.45	+ £37.66	+ £34.93
£74.22	**£51.31**	**£63.92**
£17.79	£20.58	£39.76
+£74.33	+ £69.55	+ £24.34
£92.12	**£90.13**	**£64.10**
18.48 m	23.95 m	17.68 m
+ 34.93 m	+ 27.15 m	+ 16.27 m
53.41 m	**51.10 m**	**33.95 m**
84.64 m	23.29 m	73.81 m
+ 16.38 m	+ 36.82 m	+ 26.89 m
101.02 m	**60.11 m**	**100.70 m**

Write the answer to each sum in the box.

£64.82 + £39.28 = **£104.10**   £97.47 + £29.34 = **£126.81**

£32.91 + £11.39 = **£44.30**   £52.63 + £18.57 = **£71.20**

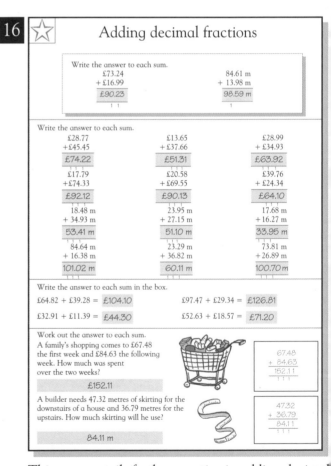

Work out the answer to each sum.

A family's shopping comes to £67.48 the first week and £84.63 the following week. How much was spent over the two weeks?

67.48
+ 84.63
152.11

£152.11

A builder needs 47.32 metres of skirting for the downstairs of a house and 36.79 metres for the upstairs. How much skirting will he use?

47.32
+ 36.79
84.11

84.11 m

This page entails further practice in adding decimal fractions and, once again, care may be needed in placing the decimal point.

17 — Subtracting decimal fractions ⭐

Write the answer to each sum.

$$\begin{array}{r} 6\,1\,1 \\ £27.23 \\ -£14.46 \\ \hline £12.77 \end{array} \qquad \begin{array}{r} 3\,1\,1 \\ 54.21\ m \\ -12.75\ m \\ \hline 41.46\ m \end{array}$$

Write the answer to each sum.

£93.52 − £41.73 **£51.79**	£79.24 − £23.75 **£55.49**	£82.63 − £30.99 **£51.64**
£55.32 − £11.54 **£43.78**	£64.23 − £20.57 **£43.66**	£42.13 − £10.26 **£31.87**
53.74 m − 21.76 m **31.98 m**	68.26 m − 32.38 m **35.88 m**	89.13 m − 34.35 m **54.78 m**
98.92 m − 42.83 m **56.09 m**	74.61 m − 22.76 m **51.85 m**	69.26 m − 25.99 m **43.27 m**

Write the answer to each sum in the box.

£64.31 − £41.32 = **£22.99**   £67.76 − £31.77 = **£35.99**

£93.18 − £31.99 = **£61.19**   £77.24 − £32.65 = **£44.59**

Work out the answer to each sum.

Deepak has saved £97.63. He spends £25.98. How much does he have left?

£71.65

$$\begin{array}{r} 97.63 \\ -25.98 \\ \hline 71.65 \end{array}$$

A roll of fabric has 95.43 metres on it. If 42.75 metres are sold, how much is left?

52.68 m

$$\begin{array}{r} 95.43 \\ -42.75 \\ \hline 52.68 \end{array}$$

As with decimal addition the most likely error will be in positioning the decimal point in horizontal sums. If, however, errors occur in the vertical sums, check that the children are not taking the top digit from the bottom, when the bottom digit is larger.

18 — ⭐ Subtracting decimal fractions

Write the answer to each sum.

$$\begin{array}{r} 7\,5\,51 \\ £84.63 \\ -£54.64 \\ \hline £29.99 \end{array} \qquad \begin{array}{r} 8\,12\,1 \\ 93.47\ m \\ -23.75\ m \\ \hline 69.72\ m \end{array}$$

Write the answer to each sum.

£84.25 − £35.64 **£48.61**	£63.78 − £24.88 **£38.90**	£84.14 − £25.78 **£58.36**
£94.56 − £35.57 **£58.99**	£82.21 − £22.48 **£59.73**	£33.21 − £13.37 **£19.84**
62.11 m − 11.96 m **50.15 m**	43.15 m − 12.26 m **30.89 m**	97.12 m − 29.25 m **67.87 m**
92.53 m − 13.74 m **78.79 m**	61.42 m − 24.63 m **36.79 m**	44.72 m − 19.84 m **24.88 m**

Write the answer to each sum in the box.

£72.31 − £33.59 = **£38.72**   £81.63 − £24.78 = **£56.85**

£81.32 − £24.99 = **£56.33**   £73.17 − £23.58 = **£49.59**

Work out the answer to each sum.

Tracy's grandmother gives her £25.50. If Tracy now has a total of £72.24, how much did she have before?

£46.74

$$\begin{array}{r} 72.24 \\ -25.50 \\ \hline 46.74 \end{array}$$

A junior school child ran a race in 57.43 seconds. A secondary school child ran the same race in 39.57 seconds. How much faster was the secondary school child?

17.86 seconds

$$\begin{array}{r} 57.43 \\ -39.57 \\ \hline 17.86 \end{array}$$

This page is similar to page 17 but some of the digits in the units column may require 'decomposition'. This means 'borrowing' or 'stealing' from the digit on the left. It is better to use the term 'stealing' since the digit is never returned.

19 — Multiplying by tens and units ⭐

Work out the answer to each sum.

$$\begin{array}{r} 56 \\ \times 32 \\ \hline 1680 \\ 112 \\ \hline 1792 \end{array} \qquad \begin{array}{r} 45 \\ \times 43 \\ \hline 1800 \\ 135 \\ \hline 1935 \end{array}$$

Work out the answer to each sum.

56 × 23 1120 168 **1288**	23 × 24 460 92 **552**	47 × 25 940 235 **1175**	84 × 22 1680 168 **1848**
73 × 34 2190 292 **2482**	52 × 35 1560 260 **1820**	64 × 33 1920 192 **2112**	51 × 32 1530 102 **1632**

Work out the answer to each sum.

41 × 62 2460 82 **2542**	65 × 54 3250 260 **3510**	72 × 68 4320 576 **4896**	84 × 71 5880 84 **5964**
92 × 63 5520 276 **5796**	57 × 82 4560 114 **4674**	38 × 94 3420 152 **3572**	26 × 75 1820 130 **1950**

Children need to understand that multiplying by 32 is the same as multiplying by 30, and by 2, and then adding the two answers. These sums multiply by the tens digit first. They can also be done by multiplying by the units first.

20 — ⭐ Multiplying by tens and units

Work out the answer to each sum.

$$\begin{array}{r} 39 \\ \times 87 \\ \hline 3120 \\ 273 \\ \hline 3393 \end{array} \qquad \begin{array}{r} 68 \\ \times 98 \\ \hline 6120 \\ 544 \\ \hline 6664 \end{array}$$

Work out the answer to each sum.

87 × 98 7830 696 **8526**	76 × 78 5320 608 **5928**	99 × 69 5940 891 **6831**	85 × 98 7650 680 **8330**
88 × 95 7920 440 **8360**	67 × 76 4690 402 **5092**	94 × 69 5640 846 **6486**	89 × 47 3560 623 **4183**

Work out the answer to each sum.

87 × 79 6090 783 **6873**	46 × 67 2760 322 **3082**	58 × 59 2900 522 **3422**	73 × 98 6570 584 **7154**
95 × 67 5700 665 **6365**	58 × 88 4640 464 **5104**	78 × 97 7020 546 **7566**	96 × 79 6720 864 **7584**

This page gives further practice of the multiplication work started on the previous page. When multiplying ensure that the children are carrying, but encourage them to write the carried figures small.

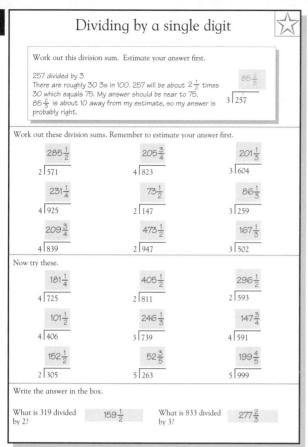

21 — Dividing by a single digit ⭐

Work out this division sum. Estimate your answer first.

257 divided by 3
There are roughly 30 3s in 100. 257 will be about $2\frac{1}{2}$ times 30 which equals 75. My answer should be near to 75.
$85\frac{2}{3}$ is about 10 away from my estimate, so my answer is probably right.

$85\frac{2}{3}$
$3\overline{)257}$

Work out these division sums. Remember to estimate your answer first.

$285\frac{1}{2}$ — $2\overline{)571}$ 　 $205\frac{3}{4}$ — $4\overline{)823}$ 　 $201\frac{1}{3}$ — $3\overline{)604}$

$231\frac{1}{4}$ — $4\overline{)925}$ 　 $73\frac{1}{2}$ — $2\overline{)147}$ 　 $86\frac{1}{3}$ — $3\overline{)259}$

$209\frac{3}{4}$ — $4\overline{)839}$ 　 $473\frac{1}{2}$ — $2\overline{)947}$ 　 $167\frac{1}{3}$ — $3\overline{)502}$

Now try these.

$181\frac{1}{4}$ — $4\overline{)725}$ 　 $405\frac{1}{2}$ — $2\overline{)811}$ 　 $296\frac{1}{2}$ — $2\overline{)593}$

$101\frac{1}{2}$ — $4\overline{)406}$ 　 $246\frac{1}{3}$ — $3\overline{)739}$ 　 $147\frac{3}{4}$ — $4\overline{)591}$

$152\frac{1}{2}$ — $2\overline{)305}$ 　 $52\frac{3}{5}$ — $5\overline{)263}$ 　 $199\frac{4}{5}$ — $5\overline{)999}$

Write the answer in the box.

What is 319 divided by 2? 　 $159\frac{1}{2}$ 　 What is 833 divided by 3? 　 $277\frac{2}{3}$

Discuss the relationship between the remainder, the divisor and the fractional answer. The answer digits must be placed above the appropriate numbers in the division box.

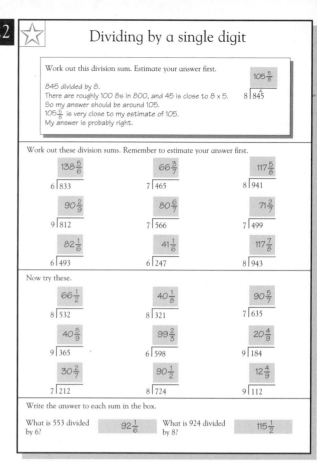

22 — ⭐ Dividing by a single digit

Work out this division sum. Estimate your answer first.

845 divided by 8.
There are roughly 100 8s in 800, and 45 is close to 8 × 5.
So my answer should be around 105.
$105\frac{5}{8}$ is very close to my estimate of 105.
My answer is probably right.

$105\frac{5}{8}$
$8\overline{)845}$

Work out these division sums. Remember to estimate your answer first.

$138\frac{5}{6}$ — $6\overline{)833}$ 　 $66\frac{3}{7}$ — $7\overline{)465}$ 　 $117\frac{5}{8}$ — $8\overline{)941}$

$90\frac{2}{3}$ — $9\overline{)812}$ 　 $80\frac{6}{7}$ — $7\overline{)566}$ 　 $71\frac{2}{7}$ — $7\overline{)499}$

$82\frac{1}{6}$ — $6\overline{)493}$ 　 $41\frac{1}{6}$ — $6\overline{)247}$ 　 $117\frac{7}{8}$ — $8\overline{)943}$

Now try these.

$66\frac{1}{2}$ — $8\overline{)532}$ 　 $40\frac{1}{8}$ — $8\overline{)321}$ 　 $90\frac{5}{7}$ — $7\overline{)635}$

$40\frac{5}{9}$ — $9\overline{)365}$ 　 $99\frac{2}{3}$ — $6\overline{)598}$ 　 $20\frac{4}{9}$ — $9\overline{)184}$

$30\frac{2}{7}$ — $7\overline{)212}$ 　 $90\frac{1}{2}$ — $8\overline{)724}$ 　 $12\frac{4}{9}$ — $9\overline{)112}$

Write the answer to each sum in the box.

What is 553 divided by 6? 　 $92\frac{1}{6}$ 　 What is 924 divided by 8? 　 $115\frac{1}{2}$

The notes on the previous page also apply to this page. In the second and third sections some of the fractional answers will need simplifying.

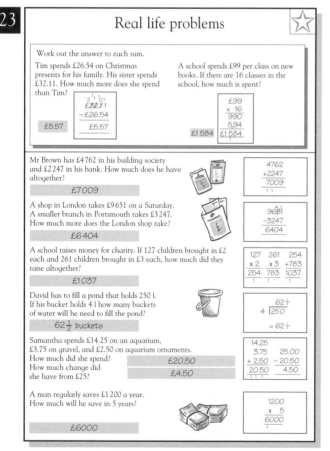

23 — Real life problems ⭐

Work out the answer to each sum.

Tim spends £26.54 on Christmas presents for his family. His sister spends £32.11. How much more does she spend than Tim?
$£32.11 - £26.54$
£5.57 　 £5.57

A school spends £99 per class on new books. If there are 16 classes in the school, how much is spent?
£99 × 16 = 990 + 594 = £1 584
£1 584 　 £1 584

Mr Brown has £4 762 in his building society and £2 247 in his bank. How much does he have altogether?
4762 + 2247 = 7009
£7 009

A shop in London takes £9 651 on a Saturday. A smaller branch in Portsmouth takes £3 247. How much more does the London shop take?
9651 − 3247 = 6404
£6 404

A school raises money for charity. If 127 children brought in £2 each and 261 children brought in £3 each, how much did they raise altogether?
127 × 2 = 254 　 261 × 3 = 783 　 254 + 783 = 1037
£1 037

David has to fill a pond that holds 250 l. If his bucket holds 4 l how many buckets of water will he need to fill the pond?
$4\overline{)250} = 62\frac{1}{2}$
$62\frac{1}{2}$ buckets

Samantha spends £14.25 on an aquarium, £3.75 on gravel, and £2.50 on aquarium ornaments. How much did she spend? How much change did she have from £25?
14.25 + 3.75 + 2.50 = 20.50 　 25.00 − 20.50 = 4.50
£20.50 　 £4.50

A man regularly saves £1 200 a year. How much will he save in 5 years?
1200 × 5 = 6000
£6 000

This page and the next provide an opportunity to apply the skills practised. Children will need to select the operation necessary. If they are unsure which operation to use, discuss whether the answer will be larger or smaller, as this narrows down the options.

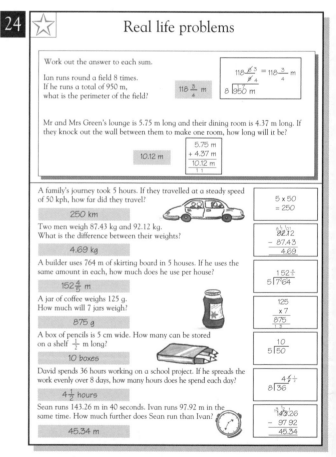

24 — ⭐ Real life problems

Work out the answer to each sum.

Ian runs round a field 8 times. If he runs a total of 950 m, what is the perimeter of the field?
$118\frac{3}{4}$ m 　 $8\overline{)950}$ m 　 $118\frac{6}{8} = 118\frac{3}{4}$ m

Mr and Mrs Green's lounge is 5.75 m long and their dining room is 4.37 m long. If they knock out the wall between them to make one room, how long will it be?
5.75 m + 4.37 m = 10.12 m
10.12 m

A family's journey took 5 hours. If they travelled at a steady speed of 50 kph, how far did they travel?
5 × 50 = 250
250 km

Two men weigh 87.43 kg and 92.12 kg. What is the difference between their weights?
92.12 − 87.43 = 4.69
4.69 kg

A builder uses 764 m of skirting board in 5 houses. If he uses the same amount in each, how much does he use per house?
$5\overline{)764} = 152\frac{4}{5}$
$152\frac{4}{5}$ m

A jar of coffee weighs 125 g. How much will 7 jars weigh?
125 × 7 = 875
875 g

A box of pencils is 5 cm wide. How many can be stored on a shelf $\frac{1}{2}$ m long?
$5\overline{)50} = 10$
10 boxes

David spends 36 hours working on a school project. If he spreads the work evenly over 8 days, how many hours does he spend each day?
$8\overline{)36} = 4\frac{4}{8} = 4\frac{1}{2}$
$4\frac{1}{2}$ hours

Sean runs 143.26 m in 40 seconds. Ivan runs 97.92 m in the same time. How much further does Sean run than Ivan?
143.26 − 97.92 = 45.34
45.34 m

As on the previous page, the skills learned up until now have been tested in situations that may be faced on a day-to-day basis.

Volumes of cubes and cuboids ⭐

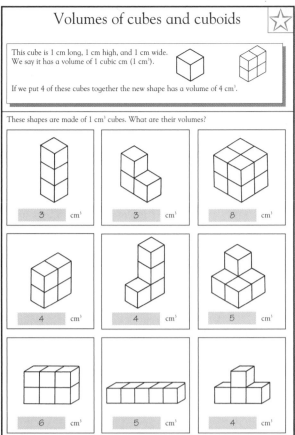

This cube is 1 cm long, 1 cm high, and 1 cm wide.
We say it has a volume of 1 cubic cm (1 cm³).

If we put 4 of these cubes together the new shape has a volume of 4 cm³.

These shapes are made of 1 cm³ cubes. What are their volumes?

3 cm³	3 cm³	8 cm³
4 cm³	4 cm³	5 cm³
6 cm³	5 cm³	4 cm³

This page introduces the concept of volume. It should be fairly straightforward and may provide a good opportunity to discuss the difference between square centimetres and cubic centimetres.

Problems with time

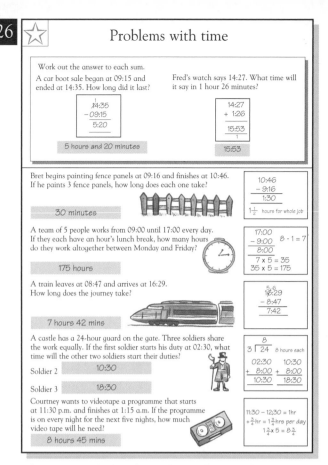

Work out the answer to each sum.

A car boot sale began at 09:15 and ended at 14:35. How long did it last?

$$\begin{array}{r} 1 \\ 14{:}35 \\ -\ 09{:}15 \\ \hline 5{:}20 \end{array}$$

5 hours and 20 minutes

Fred's watch says 14:27. What time will it say in 1 hour 26 minutes?

$$\begin{array}{r} 14{:}27 \\ +\ 1{:}26 \\ \hline 15{:}53 \\ \hline 1 \end{array}$$

15:53

Bret begins painting fence panels at 09:16 and finishes at 10:46. If he paints 3 fence panels, how long does each one take?

30 minutes

$$\begin{array}{r} 10{:}46 \\ -\ 9{:}16 \\ \hline 1{:}30 \end{array}$$
1½ hours for whole job

A team of 5 people works from 09:00 until 17:00 every day. If they each have an hour's lunch break, how many hours do they work altogether between Monday and Friday?

175 hours

$$\begin{array}{r} 17{:}00 \\ -\ 9{:}00 \\ \hline 8{:}00 \end{array} \quad 8 - 1 = 7$$
$7 \times 5 = 35$
$35 \times 5 = 175$

A train leaves at 08:47 and arrives at 16:29. How long does the journey take?

7 hours 42 mins

$$\begin{array}{r} {}^{5\ 6}16{:}29 \\ -\ 8{:}47 \\ \hline 7{:}42 \end{array}$$

A castle has a 24-hour guard on the gate. Three soldiers share the work equally. If the first soldier starts his duty at 02:30, what time will the other two soldiers start their duties?

Soldier 2   10:30

Soldier 3   18:30

$$3\,\overline{)\,24}\ \ \ 8\ \text{hours each}$$
$$\begin{array}{r} 02{:}30 \\ +\ 8{:}00 \\ \hline 10{:}30 \end{array} \quad \begin{array}{r} 10{:}30 \\ +\ 8{:}00 \\ \hline 18{:}30 \end{array}$$

Courtney wants to videotape a programme that starts at 11:30 p.m. and finishes at 1:15 a.m. If the programme is on every night for the next five nights, how much video tape will he need?

8 hours 45 mins

11:30 – 12:30 = 1hr
+ ¾ hr = 1¾ hrs per day
1¾ × 5 = 8¾

This page includes the 24-hour clock with which children should be familiar. In some questions children may prefer 'counting on' to subtraction. Allow whichever method they are most comfortable with, as long as the answer is correct.

Looking at graphs ⭐

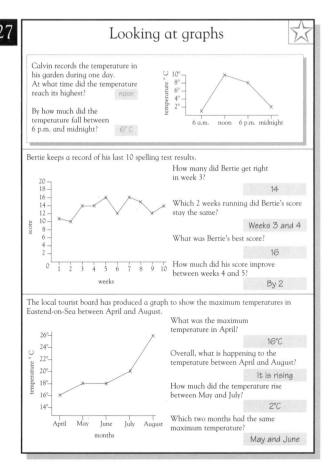

Calvin records the temperature in his garden during one day. At what time did the temperature reach its highest?   noon

By how much did the temperature fall between 6 p.m. and midnight?   6° C

Bertie keeps a record of his last 10 spelling test results.

How many did Bertie get right in week 3?   14

Which 2 weeks running did Bertie's score stay the same?   Weeks 3 and 4

What was Bertie's best score?   16

How much did his score improve between weeks 4 and 5?   By 2

The local tourist board has produced a graph to show the maximum temperatures in Eastend-on-Sea between April and August.

What was the maximum temperature in April?   16°C

Overall, what is happening to the temperature between April and August?   It is rising

How much did the temperature rise between May and July?   2°C

Which two months had the same maximum temperature?   May and June

This page should be fairly straightforward. The most likely errors will arise from a misreading of the graph.

Nets of simple shapes

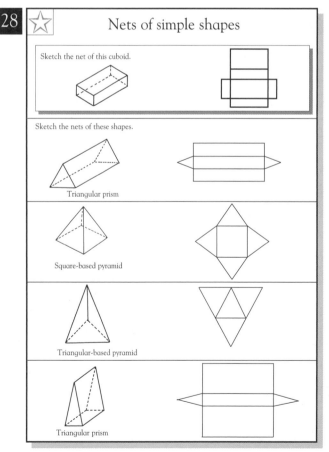

Sketch the net of this cuboid.

Sketch the nets of these shapes.

Triangular prism

Square-based pyramid

Triangular-based pyramid

Triangular prism

If children experience problems on this page, it may be necessary to draw the nets on paper or card, and cut them out to see if they make the shape. If this is done, point out that nets do not require flaps.

More nets of simple shapes

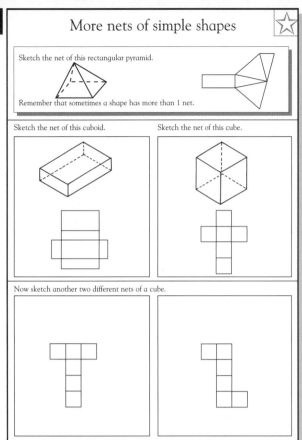

Sketch the net of this rectangular pyramid.

Remember that sometimes a shape has more than 1 net.

Sketch the net of this cuboid.

Sketch the net of this cube.

Now sketch another two different nets of a cube.

These are the three likely nets of a cube that children may sketch; however, others are acceptable. If in doubt, sketch on squared paper and cut out to see of it will make a cube. If children found the previous page difficult, continue with the practical work.

Rotational symmetry

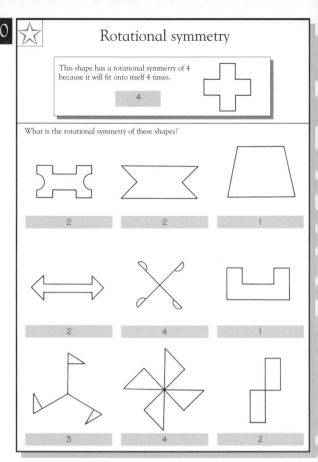

This shape has a rotational symmetry of 4 because it will fit onto itself 4 times.

4

What is the rotational symmetry of these shapes?

2   2   1

2   4   1

3   4   2

If children are confused, the shape can be traced and the tracing paper placed over the original shape to show the order of rotation.

Acute and obtuse angles

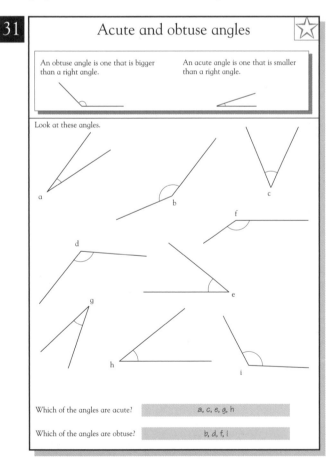

An obtuse angle is one that is bigger than a right angle.

An acute angle is one that is smaller than a right angle.

Look at these angles.

a, b, c, d, e, f, g, h, i

Which of the angles are acute?   a, c, e, g, h

Which of the angles are obtuse?   b, d, f, i

Tell children who confuse acute and obtuse angles that acute angles look like sharp pencils (acute meaning sharp) and obtuse angles look like blunt pencils (obtuse meaning blunt). Use a paper or card right angle to compare with the angles shown.

Acute and obtuse angles

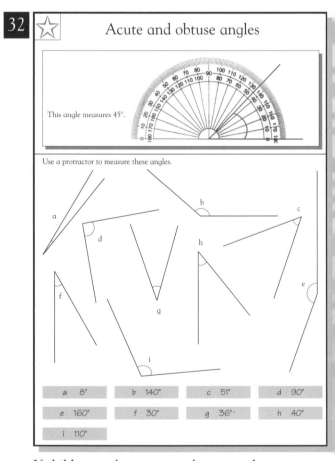

This angle measures 45°.

Use a protractor to measure these angles.

a 8°	b 140°	c 51°	d 90°
e 160°	f 30°	g 36°	h 40°
i 110°			

If children make errors on this page, the two most likely reasons are that they have placed the protractor inaccurately over the angle, or that they have read off the angle from the wrong direction.

Subtracting decimal fractions

Write the answer to each sum.

$$
\begin{array}{r}
{}^{6}{}^{1}1{}^{1}1 \\
£27.23 \\
-\;£14.46 \\
\hline
£12.77
\end{array}
\qquad
\begin{array}{r}
3{}^{1}1{}^{1}1 \\
54.21\ \text{m} \\
-\;12.75\ \text{m} \\
\hline
41.46\ \text{m}
\end{array}
$$

Write the answer to each sum.

$$
\begin{array}{r}
£93.52 \\
-\;£41.73 \\
\hline
\end{array}
\qquad
\begin{array}{r}
£79.24 \\
-\;£23.75 \\
\hline
\end{array}
\qquad
\begin{array}{r}
£82.63 \\
-\;£30.99 \\
\hline
\end{array}
$$

$$
\begin{array}{r}
£55.32 \\
-\;£11.54 \\
\hline
\end{array}
\qquad
\begin{array}{r}
£64.23 \\
-\;£20.57 \\
\hline
\end{array}
\qquad
\begin{array}{r}
£42.13 \\
-\;£10.26 \\
\hline
\end{array}
$$

$$
\begin{array}{r}
53.74\ \text{m} \\
-21.76\ \text{m} \\
\hline
\end{array}
\qquad
\begin{array}{r}
68.26\ \text{m} \\
-\;32.38\ \text{m} \\
\hline
\end{array}
\qquad
\begin{array}{r}
89.13\ \text{m} \\
-\;34.35\ \text{m} \\
\hline
\end{array}
$$

$$
\begin{array}{r}
98.92\ \text{m} \\
-\;42.83\ \text{m} \\
\hline
\end{array}
\qquad
\begin{array}{r}
74.61\ \text{m} \\
-\;22.76\ \text{m} \\
\hline
\end{array}
\qquad
\begin{array}{r}
69.26\ \text{m} \\
-\;25.99\ \text{m} \\
\hline
\end{array}
$$

Write the answer to each sum in the box.

£64.31 – £41.32 =   £67.76 – £31.77 =

£93.18 – £31.99 =   £77.24 – £32.65 =

Work out the answer to each sum.

Deepak has saved £97.63. He spends £25.98. How much does he have left?

A roll of fabric has 95.43 metres on it. If 42.75 metres are sold, how much is left?

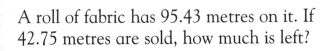

Subtracting decimal fractions

Write the answer to each sum.

£84.25 − £35.64	£63.78 − £24.88	£84.14 − £25.78
£94.56 − £35.57	£82.21 − £22.48	£33.21 − £13.37
62.11 m − 11.96 m	43.15 m − 12.26 m	97.12 m − 29.25 m
92.53 m − 13.74 m	61.42 m − 24.63 m	44.72 m − 19.84 m

Write the answer to each sum in the box.

£72.31 − £33.59 =

£81.63 − £24.78 =

£81.32 − £24.99 =

£73.17 − £23.58 =

Work out the answer to each sum.
Tracy's grandmother gives her £25.50.
If Tracy now has a total of £72.24,
how much did she have before?

A junior school child ran a race in 57.43 seconds. A secondary
school child ran the same race in 39.57 seconds. How much faster
was the secondary school child?

Multiplying by tens and units

Work out the answer to each sum.

```
    56          45
  x 32        x 43
  1680        1800
   11 2        1 35
  1792        1935
```

Work out the answer to each sum.

```
    56          23          47          84
  x 23        x 24        x 25        x 22
     0           0           0           0
```

```
    73          52          64          51
  x 34        x 35        x 33        x 32
     0           0           0           0
```

Work out the answer to each sum.

```
    41          65          72          84
  x 62        x 54        x 68        x 71
```

```
    92          57          38          26
  x 63        x 82        x 94        x 75
```

Multiplying by tens and units

Work out the answer to each sum.

```
      39              68
    x 87            x 98
    3 1,20          6 1,20
      7               7
      273             544
      6               6
    3 393           6 664
```

Work out the answer to each sum.

```
    87          76          99          85
  x 98        x 78        x 69        x 98
    0           0           0           0
```

```
    88          67          94          89
  x 95        x 76        x 69        x 47
    0           0           0           0
```

Work out the answer to each sum.

```
    87          46          58          73
  x 79        x 67        x 59        x 98
```

```
    95          58          78          96
  x 67        x 88        x 97        x 79
```

20

Dividing by a single digit

Work out this division sum. Estimate your answer first.

257 divided by 3
There are roughly 30 3s in 100. 257 will be about $2\frac{1}{2}$ times
30 which equals 75. My answer should be near to 75.
$85\frac{2}{3}$ is about 10 away from my estimate, so my answer is
probably right.

$85\frac{2}{3}$

$3\overline{)25^{1}7}$

Work out these division sums. Remember to estimate your answer first.

$2\overline{)571}$ $4\overline{)823}$ $3\overline{)604}$

$4\overline{)925}$ $2\overline{)147}$ $3\overline{)259}$

$4\overline{)839}$ $2\overline{)947}$ $3\overline{)502}$

Now try these.

$4\overline{)725}$ $2\overline{)811}$ $2\overline{)593}$

$4\overline{)406}$ $3\overline{)739}$ $4\overline{)591}$

$2\overline{)305}$ $5\overline{)263}$ $5\overline{)999}$

Write the answer in the box.

What is 319 divided
by 2?

What is 833 divided
by 3?

21

Dividing by a single digit

Work out this division sum. Estimate your answer first.

845 divided by 8.
There are roughly 100 8s in 800, and 45 is close to 8 x 5.
So my answer should be around 105.
105 $\frac{5}{8}$ is very close to my estimate of 105.
My answer is probably right.

$105\frac{5}{8}$

$8\overline{)8\overset{4}{4}5}$

Work out these division sums. Remember to estimate your answer first.

$6\overline{)833}$ $7\overline{)465}$ $8\overline{)941}$

$9\overline{)812}$ $7\overline{)566}$ $7\overline{)499}$

$6\overline{)493}$ $6\overline{)247}$ $8\overline{)943}$

Now try these.

$8\overline{)532}$ $8\overline{)321}$ $7\overline{)635}$

$9\overline{)365}$ $6\overline{)598}$ $9\overline{)184}$

$7\overline{)212}$ $8\overline{)724}$ $9\overline{)112}$

Write the answer to each sum in the box.

What is 553 divided by 6?

What is 924 divided by 8?

Real life problems

Work out the answer to each sum.

Tim spends £26.54 on Christmas presents for his family. His sister spends £32.11. How much more does she spend than Tim?

$$
\begin{array}{r}
2\,{}^{1}1\,{}^{1}01 \\
£32.11 \\
-£26.54 \\
\hline
£5.57
\end{array}
$$

£5.57

A school spends £99 per class on new books. If there are 16 classes in the school, how much is spent?

$$
\begin{array}{r}
£99 \\
\times\ 16 \\
\hline
990 \\
594 \\
\hline
£1\,584 \\
{}^{1}
\end{array}
$$

£1 584

Mr Brown has £4 762 in his building society and £2 247 in his bank. How much does he have altogether?

A shop in London takes £9 651 on a Saturday. A smaller branch in Portsmouth takes £3 247. How much more does the London shop take?

A school raises money for charity. If 127 children brought in £2 each and 261 children brought in £3 each, how much did they raise altogether?

David has to fill a pond that holds 250 l. If his bucket holds 4 l how many buckets of water will he need to fill the pond?

Samantha spends £14.25 on an aquarium, £3.75 on gravel, and £2.50 on aquarium ornaments. How much did she spend? How much change did she have from £25?

A man regularly saves £1 200 a year. How much will he save in 5 years?

Real life problems

Work out the answer to each sum.

Ian runs round a field 8 times.
If he runs a total of 950 m,
what is the perimeter of the field?

$118 \frac{3}{4}$ m

$$118\frac{\cancel{6}\,^{3}}{\cancel{8}\,_{4}} = 118\frac{3}{4} \text{ m}$$

$$8\overline{\smash{\big)}950} \text{ m}$$

Mr and Mrs Green's lounge is 5.75 m long and their dining room is 4.37 m long. If they knock out the wall between them to make one room, how long will it be?

10.12 m

$$\begin{array}{r} 5.75 \text{ m} \\ + 4.37 \text{ m} \\ \hline 10.12 \text{ m} \\ {\scriptstyle 1\ 1} \end{array}$$

A family's journey took 5 hours. If they travelled at a steady speed of 50 kph, how far did they travel?

Two men weigh 87.43 kg and 92.12 kg.
What is the difference between their weights?

A builder uses 764 m of skirting board in 5 houses. If he uses the same amount in each, how much does he use per house?

A jar of coffee weighs 125 g.
How much will 7 jars weigh?

A box of pencils is 5 cm wide. How many can be stored on a shelf $\frac{1}{2}$ m long?

David spends 36 hours working on a school project. If he spreads the work evenly over 8 days, how many hours does he spend each day?

Sean runs 143.26 m in 40 seconds. Ivan runs 97.92 m in the same time. How much further does Sean run than Ivan?

Volumes of cubes and cuboids

This cube is 1 cm long, 1 cm high, and 1 cm wide. We say it has a volume of 1 cubic cm (1 cm³).

If we put 4 of these cubes together the new shape has a volume of 4 cm³.

These shapes are made of 1 cm³ cubes. What are their volumes?

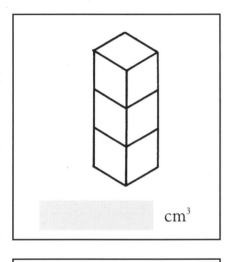

_____ cm³

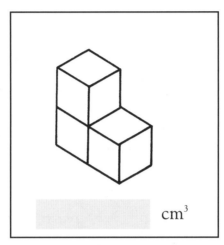

_____ cm³

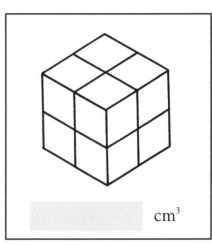

_____ cm³

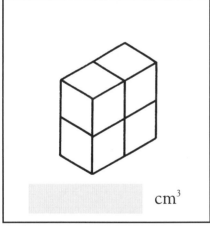

_____ cm³

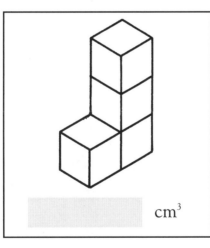

_____ cm³

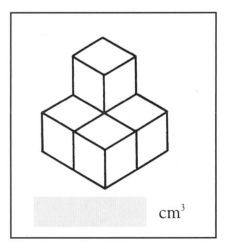

_____ cm³

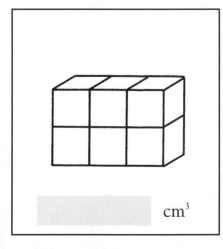

_____ cm³

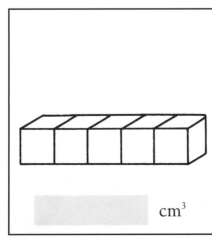

_____ cm³

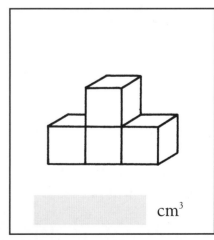

_____ cm³

Problems with time

Work out the answer to each sum.

A car boot sale began at 09:15 and ended at 14:35. How long did it last?

```
  1
 14:35
- 09:15
 ─────
  5:20
```

5 hours and 20 minutes

Fred's watch says 14:27. What time will it say in 1 hour 26 minutes?

```
 14:27
+ 1:26
 ─────
 15:53
     1
```

15:53

Bret begins painting fence panels at 09:16 and finishes at 10:46. If he paints 3 fence panels, how long does each one take?

A team of 5 people works from 09:00 until 17:00 every day. If they each have an hour's lunch break, how many hours do they work altogether between Monday and Friday?

A train leaves at 08:47 and arrives at 16:29. How long does the journey take?

A castle has a 24-hour guard on the gate. Three soldiers share the work equally. If the first soldier starts his duty at 02:30, what time will the other two soldiers start their duties?

Soldier 2

Soldier 3

Courtney wants to videotape a programme that starts at 11:30 p.m. and finishes at 1:15 a.m. If the programme is on every night for the next five nights, how much video tape will he need?

Looking at graphs

Calvin records the temperature in his garden during one day.
At what time did the temperature reach its highest?   *noon*

By how much did the temperature fall between 6 p.m. and midnight?   *6° C*

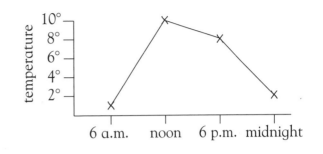

Bertie keeps a record of his last 10 spelling test results.

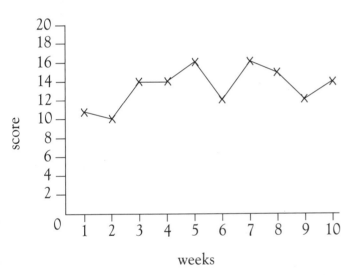

How many did Bertie get right in week 3?

Which 2 weeks running did Bertie's score stay the same?

What was Bertie's best score?

How much did his score improve between weeks 4 and 5?

The local tourist board has produced a graph to show the maximum temperatures in Eastend-on-Sea between April and August.

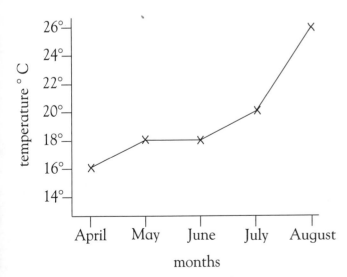

What was the maximum temperature in April?

Overall, what is happening to the temperature between April and August?

How much did the temperature rise between May and July?

Which two months had the same maximum temperature?

Nets of simple shapes

Sketch the net of this cuboid.

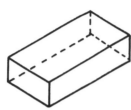

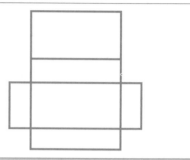

Sketch the nets of these shapes.

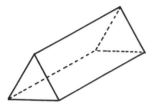

Triangular prism

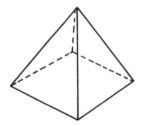

Square-based pyramid

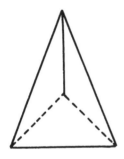

Triangular-based pyramid

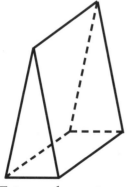

Triangular prism

More nets of simple shapes

Sketch the net of this rectangular pyramid.

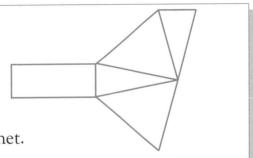

Remember that sometimes a shape has more than 1 net.

Sketch the net of this cuboid.

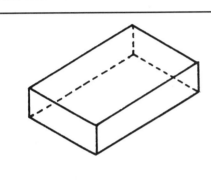

Sketch the net of this cube.

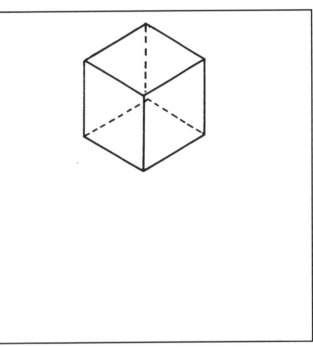

Now sketch another two different nets of a cube.

Rotational symmetry

This shape has a rotational symmetry of 4 because it will fit onto itself 4 times.

4

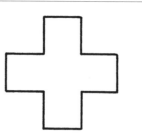

What is the rotational symmetry of these shapes?

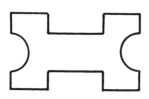

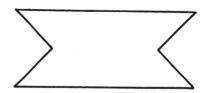

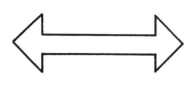

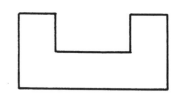

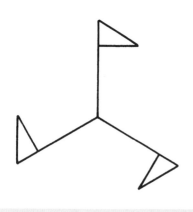

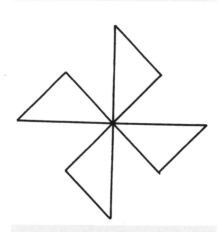

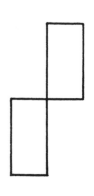

Acute and obtuse angles

An obtuse angle is one that is bigger than a right angle.

An acute angle is one that is smaller than a right angle.

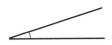

Look at these angles.

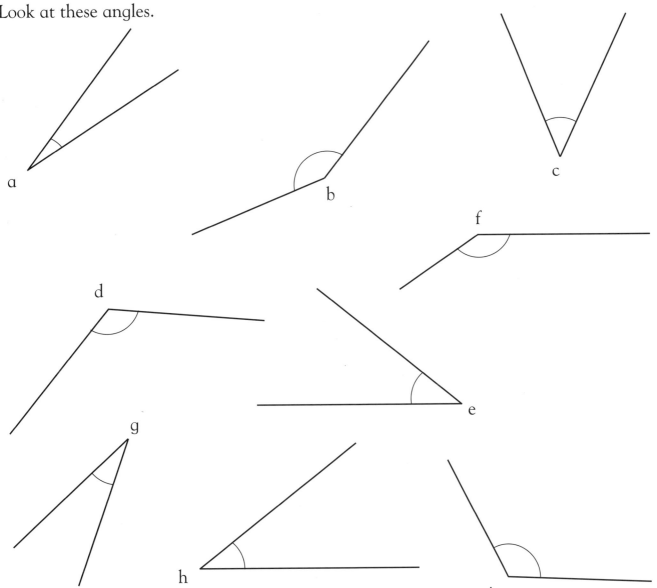

a

b

c

d

f

e

g

h

i

Which of the angles are acute?

Which of the angles are obtuse?

Acute and obtuse angles

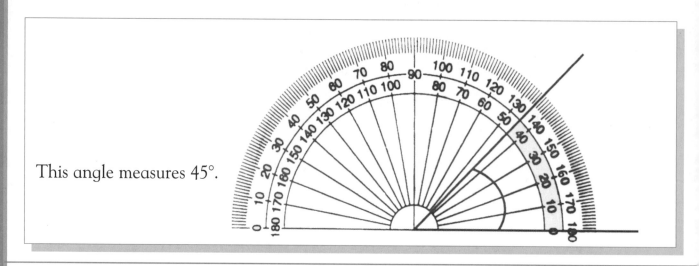

This angle measures 45°.

Use a protractor to measure these angles.

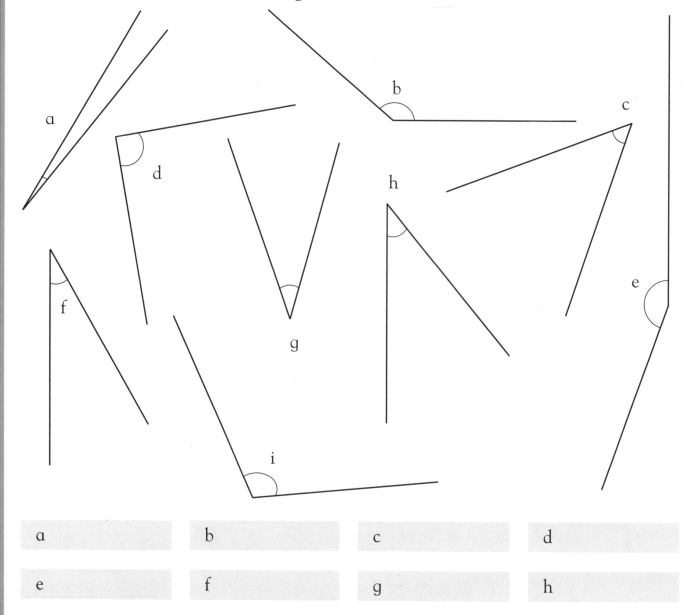

a		b		c		d	

e		f		g		h	

i	